American Inside Out Evolution

Workbook

Beginner

SUE KAY
VAUGHAN JONES
PETER MAGGS
CATHERINE SMITH

macmillan education

Contents

Unit	Grammar & Vocabulary	Listening	Writing & Pronunciation
1 ID page 4	**G** *my/your/his/her* Singular and plural nouns. *this/these* **V** Numbers 1–10. Everyday objects	Asking about name, telephone number, and possessions	**P** Singular and plural nouns
2 International page 7	**G** *be:* simple present. *How much ...?* **V** Countries. Nationalities. Numbers 11–199		**W** Using question marks and periods Writing short questions and answers **P** Word stress: syllables
3 Family page 10	**G** *How old ...?* Possessive *'s/s', our/their. have/has* **V** Family	Conversations about family	**P** Sounds /ʌ/ and /æ/
4 Life page 13	**G** Simple present: *I, he, she, it, you, we, they.* The time. **V** Jobs. Common verbs		**W** Building a description of a daily routine from notes **P** Rhyming words
5 Places page 16	**G** *There's/there are. some/any* **V** Places in a city. Verb phrases with *go*	A visit to Paris	**P** Sounds /eɪ/ and /aɪ/
6 Clothes page 19	**G** Present progressive *How often ...?* Adverbs of frequency. **V** Colors. Clothes. Verb phrases		**W** Posting on Instagram **P** Sounds /oʊ/ and /aʊ/

1 ID

Grammar

1 Write the correct word.

a A: What's **(his / her)** her name?
B: **(His / Her)** Her name's Kate.

b A: What's **(your / my)** _____ name?
B: **(Your / My)** _____ name's Jim.

c A: What's **(his / her)** _____ name?
B: **(His / Her)** _____ name's Luis.

d A: What's **(your / her)** _____ name?
B: **(My / Her)** _____ name's Maria.

2 Complete the questions with *this* or *these*.

a What's ________?
b What are ________?

3 Complete the sentences with *It's* or *They're*.

a It's a passport.
b ________ keys.
c ________ a cell phone.
d ________ books.
e ________ pens.
f ________ a computer.

4 Match the questions in Exercise 2 with the answers in Exercise 3.

a What's this?
It's a passport.
b ____________________
____
c ____________________
____
d ____________________
____
e ____________________
____
f ____________________
____

Vocabulary

1 Label the pictures *(a-h)* with the words in the box.

bag	book	camera	cell phone
computer	key	~~passport~~	pen

a passport

b ______

c ______

d ______

e ______

f ______

g ______

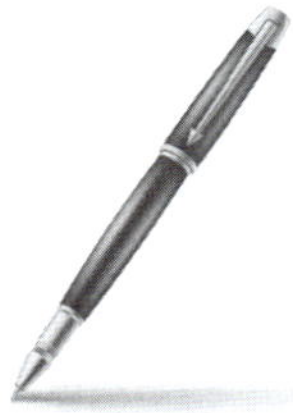

h ______

2 Write the numbers in words.

1 2 3 4 5 6 7 8 9 10

1 one
2 ______
3 ______
4 ______
5 ______
6 ______
7 ______
8 ______
9 ______
10 ______

3 Label the pictures.

a seven keys

b ______

c ______

d ______

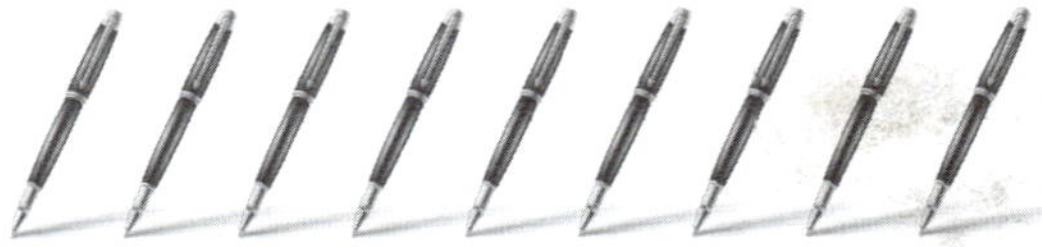

e ______

f ______

g ______

h ______

Listening

1 02-03 Cover the listening script. Listen and match the conversations *(1-2)* to the pictures *(a-b)*.

Conversation 1: picture _____

Conversation 2: picture _____

a

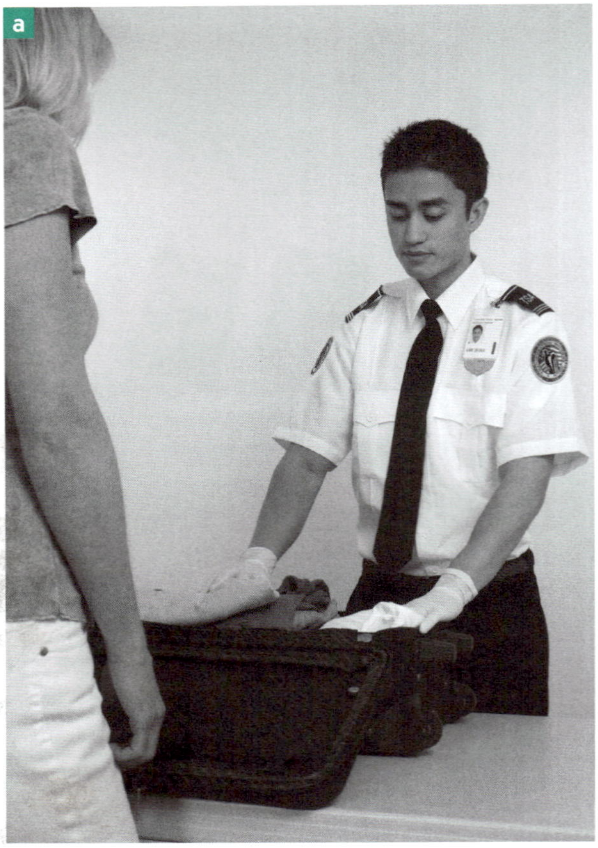

b

Conversation 1

Woman: Hello. Can I help you?
Man: I'm here to see Dr. Jones.
Woman: OK. What's your name?
Man: Mr. Smith.
Woman: And what's your first name, Mr. Smith?
Man: Marcus.
Woman: Can you spell that, please?
Man: M-A-R-C-U-S.
Woman: What's your telephone number?
Man: My home telephone is 304-556-7587 and my cell phone number is 304-291-0081.

Conversation 2

Woman: That's my bag!
Man: Hmm. What's in your bag?
Woman: Er, my keys, my camera, my book ... oh, and my cell phone.
Man: What's your name?
Woman: Elise Brooker.
Man: What's your cell phone number?
Woman: 212-690-5400.
Man: 212-690-5400. Right. Yes, it's your bag. Here you go.
Woman: Thank you.

2 Listen again and underline the correct answers.

Conversation 1

a What's his first name?
Smith / Jim / Marcus

b What's his last name?
Smith / Marcus / Brown

Conversation 2

c What's her first name?
Elise / Brooker / Mary

d What's her last name?
Elise / Potter / Brooker

3 Listen again. Are the sentences true (T) or false (F)?

a Marcus Smith's home telephone number is 305-557-7987. __F__

b Marcus Smith's cell phone numbers is 304-281-0081. _____

c Elise Brooker's computer is in her bag. _____

d Elise Brooker's book is in her bag. _____

e Elise Brooker's telephone number is 212-690-6400. _____

Pronunciation

1 04 Listen and underline the word you hear.

a pen / pens
b book / books
c name / names
d cell phone / cell phones
e passport / passports
f camera / cameras

2 Practice the words in Exercise 1.

2 International

Grammar

1 **Complete the table with the simple present of the verb *be*.**

	Full form	Contraction
I	am	I'm
you		
he/she/it		
we		
they		

2 **Complete the sentences. Use contractions.**

a She's from Spain.
b Jorge____ from Brazil.
c I____ from Mexico.
d We____ from Japan.
e They____ from Chile.
f It____ from Germany.

3 **Complete the questions. Use full forms.**

a Where are you from?
b Are you from Germany?
c Where _______ Josefina from?
d Where _______ Karl and Marta from?
e _______ he from Mexico?
f _______ they from Spain?

4 **Write answers to the questions.**

a Are you Japanese?
No, I'm not.
b Is she Brazilian?
Yes, ______________________.
c Are you Mexican?
Yes, ______________________.
d Are you English?
No, ______________________.
e Are they Chilean?
No, ______________________.
f Where are you from?
I'm from ______________________.

5 **Write questions and answers.**

a

a cappuccino in London
How much is a cappuccino in London?

b

a hamburger in New York City
____

c

a movie ticket in Hong Kong
____

d

donuts in Buenos Aires
____

e

a cell phone in Madrid
____

f

pens in Paris
____

6 **Write about the prices of the things in Exercise 5 in your country.**

a A cappuccino is six dollars.
b ______________________
c ______________________
d ______________________
e ______________________
f ______________________

Vocabulary

1 Find the names of countries in the wordsnake.

BRAZIL/MEXICOJAPANGERMANYCHILESPAIN

a Brazil

b ______

c ______

d ______

e ______

f ______

2 Write sentences about the people's nationality.

a 

Kate and Tim – Britain

They're British.

b 

Naomi – the USA

______

c 

Ana Sophia – Brazil

______

d 

Adriano – Spain

______

e 

Kenji – Japan

______

f 

Franz – Germany

______

g 

Gracia – Mexico

______

3 Write the missing numbers.

a eleven, twelve, thirteen fourteen

b fifteen, sixteen, seventeen, ______

c twenty-four, twenty-five, ______

d ten, ______, thirty, forty

e ______, eighty, ninety

f fifty-eight, fifty-nine, ______

g thirty-one, ______, thirty-three

h ninety-eight, ninety-nine, ______

4 Write the numbers in words.

a 16 sixteen

b 11 ______

c 36 ______

d 49 ______

e 78 ______

f 89 ______

5 Complete the conversation using the words in the box.

are	How	is	~~much~~	thanks

Man: How (1) much is this?

Sales Clerk: Seventy dollars.

Man: OK, (2) ______. (3) ______ much (4) ______ this bag?

Sales Clerk: Eighty-nine dollars.

Man: Oh. How much (5) ______ these?

Sales Clerk: One hundred and ninety-five dollars.

Man: Oh! OK, no thanks.

Writing

Using question marks and periods
Writing short questions and answers

1 **Read the sentences. Circle the question marks and underline the periods.**

a How much is a cappuccino(?)
b He's from Brazil.
c Is she Mexican?
d Where are they from?
e The cameras are from Japan.

2 **Complete the rules using the words in the box.**

period	question mark

a You use a ______________ at the end of a question.
b You use a ______________ at the end of a sentence.

3 **Write the words in the correct order. Put a question mark or a period at the end of a sentence.**

a your What's name
What's your name?

b you Where from are
____

c you Australia from Are
____

d from I'm Chile
____

e Reiko name's My
____

f from Germany I'm No,
____

4 **Match the questions and answers in Exercise 3.**

1 Question: What's your name?
Answer: ______________________________

2 Question: ______________________________
Answer: ______________________________

3 Question: ______________________________
Answer: ______________________________

5 **Write true answers to the questions in Exercise 4.**

Answer: ______________________________
____

Answer: ______________________________
____

Answer: ______________________________
____

Pronunciation

1 **Count the number of syllables in each word. Write the number in the box.**

a computer [3]
b American [ ]
c nationality [ ]
d Mexican [ ]
e movie [ ]
f seventy [ ]
g question [ ]
h Argentina [ ]
i eleven [ ]
j conversation [ ]

05 **Listen, check, and repeat.**

2 **Listen again and underline the stressed syllables in Exercise 1.**

a com**pu**ter

3 Family

Grammar

1 Write questions with *How old is / are …?*

a your brother
How old is your brother?

b your sister
____

c your car
____

d your parents
____

e you
____

f your cell phone
____

g your children
____

h your computer
____

2 Write true answers to five questions in Exercise 1.

a My brother is 37.

3 Complete the table.

Subject pronoun	Possessive determiner
I	my
you	
he	
she	
it	its
we	
they	

4 Complete the text with words from Exercise 3.

Hi, (1) __my__ name's Tom Braddock. This is (2)________ family. This is Judy. (3) ________'s my wife. These are (4) ________ children. (5) ________ names are Jack, Jenny, and Sonya. (6) ________'re from Atlanta. (7) ________'s in the USA. My parents are Lynn and Bill. (8) ________'re from California.

06 Listen and check.

5 Underline the correct word.

a Tom's **mother's / mothers'** name is Lynn.
b Jack's **sister's / sisters'** names are Jenny and Sonya.
c Judy is **Tom's / Toms'** wife.
d The **children's / childrens'** names are Jack, Jenny and Sonya.
e Their **grandparent's / grandparents'** names are Lynn and Bill.

6 Complete the sentences with *have* or *has*.

a I __have__ a Japanese car.
b My brother ________ two dogs.
c You ________ one sister.
d They ________ four children.
e We ________ a new camera.
f Ana ________ an old computer.
g Our book ________ six units.

Pronunciation

1 ▶ 07 Listen to the sounds /ʌ/ and /æ/.

/ʌ/ number
/æ/ married

2 ▶ 08 Listen to the words in the box. Is the underlined sound /ʌ/ or /æ/? Put the words in the correct column.

~~bag~~	bus	camera	country
family	grandfather	husband	Japan
mother	much	son	thank
that			

/ʌ/	/æ/
bus	bag

▶ 09 Listen, check, and repeat.

Vocabulary

1 Find twelve family words in the wordsquare and complete the table below. Look → and ↓.

A	G	R	A	N	F	T	G	H	S	T	E	R	G
P	G	P	R	E	T	S	I	S	M	Q	D	A	R
G	R	A	N	D	M	O	T	H	E	R	A	U	A
H	A	P	H	H	U	S	B	A	N	D	U	G	N
S	N	S	O	N	B	D	H	T	R	H	G	H	D
A	D	M	O	G	R	W	I	F	E	T	H	T	D
Q	F	A	J	N	O	P	G	M	H	L	T	G	A
W	A	M	H	R	T	O	H	O	T	P	E	R	U
E	T	A	L	A	H	P	T	I	A	Y	R	A	G
I	H	N	O	N	E	S	U	N	F	V	S	T	H
N	E	S	U	D	R	F	R	E	G	H	J	H	T
P	R	T	S	M	O	T	H	E	R	E	M	E	E
G	R	A	F	A	T	H	E	R	I	F	E	R	R
D	F	T	D	Q	N	O	S	D	N	A	R	G	O

♂	♀
grandfather	grandmother

2 Complete the family words.

a ch_i_ldren
b p__r__nts
c gr__ndp__r__nts
d gr__ndch__ldr__n

3 Match the sentences (a–e) with the pictures (1–5).

1

2

3

4

5

a My grandchildren are Mia, Rosa, Danny, and Sam.
Picture 3

b This is me with my parents.
Picture ______

c Our grandparents are from Colombia. Their names are Consuela and Manuel.
Picture ______

d I have two children: a son and a daughter.
Picture ______

e My daughter's name is Molly. Her dog's name is Spot.
Picture ______

4 Write five sentences about your family.

Listening

1 10-13 Cover the listening script. Listen to the conversations. Number the pictures in the order they happen (1–4).

Conversation 1

Fabio: I want to meet your family.
Anita: Really?
Fabio: Yes!
Anita: OK. Come with me to my parents' house. You can meet my parents, my grandparents and my little sister.
Fabio: Great!

Conversation 2

Anita: Hi, everyone. This is Fabio. Fabio, this is my–
Fabio: Ah, you must be Anita's grandfather.
Anita's dad: No, I'm her dad.
Fabio: Oh, I'm sorry!
Anita's dad: Don't worry. It's my gray beard. A lot of people think I'm a grandfather. My name's Pedro.
Fabio: Nice to meet you, Pedro.

Conversation 3

Anita: And this is my mom, Julia.
Fabio: It's nice to meet you.
Anita's mom: Lovely to meet you too, Fabio. You can call me Mom.
Fabio: Um... OK... Mom.

Conversation 4

Anita's sister: I'm Lara. I'm Anita's sister.
Fabio: Hi, Lara. How old are you?
Anita's sister: I'm eight.
Fabio: Wow, that's old!
Anita: No, it isn't. Come and meet Sasha. She's really old.
Fabio: Who's Sasha? Is she your grandmother?
Anita's sister: No, she's not my grandmother! She's my dog!

2 Listen again. Are the sentences true (T) or false (F)?

a Fabio wants to meet Anita's family. __F__
b Fabio is Anita's boyfriend. ______
c Fabio thinks Anita's dad is her grandfather. ______
d Fabio wants to call Anita's mother Mom. ______
e Lara is very old. ______
f Fabio meets Anita's grandmother. ______

3 Listen again and complete the sentences with the names in the box.

Fabio	Anita	Pedro	Lara	Julia

a Julia is __Pedro's__ wife.
b Sasha is ______'s dog.
c Lara is ______'s sister.
d Pedro is ______'s husband.
e Anita is ______'s girlfriend.

4 Life

Grammar

1 Complete the sentences with the words in the box.

eat	like	have	live	speak	~~work~~

a I *work* for a German company.
b He ___________ Spanish.
c We ___________ meat.
d She ___________ soccer.
e They ___________ in Bogotá.
f You ___________ two sisters.

2 Write the sentences in Exercise 1 in the negative.

a *I don't work for a German company.*
b ______________________________
c ______________________________
d ______________________________
e ______________________________
f ______________________________

3 Write questions using *Do* or *Does*.

a he / work in an office
Does he work in an office?
b the movie / start at 7 o'clock
____
c they / finish work early
____
d Rob and Jodi / live in New York
____
e she / go home on the bus
____
f you / speak English
____

4 Complete the short answers to the questions in Exercise 3.

a No, *he doesn't.*
b Yes, ______________________
c Yes, ______________________
d No, ______________________
e No, ______________________
f Yes, ______________________

5 Look at the clocks and write the times.

a 

It's seven forty-five.
It's a quarter to eight.

b 

____
____

c 

____
____

d 

____
____

e 

____
____

f 

____
____

Pronunciation

1 ▶ 14 Listen and repeat.

eat	~~flower~~	for	~~hour~~	meet	name
night	not	one	same	son	two
what	white	you	your		

Find pairs of rhyming words in the box

a *flower* and *hour*
b ___________ and ___________
c ___________ and ___________
d ___________ and ___________
e ___________ and ___________
f ___________ and ___________
g ___________ and ___________
h ___________ and ___________

2 ▶ 15 Listen, check, and repeat.

Vocabulary

1 Look at the pictures and complete the crossword with the names of the jobs.

ACROSS

DOWN

2 Find the days of the week and write them in order.

~~daMyon~~
Tedayus
eWdanedys
dursaThy
yidFar
aySurdat
dunSay

Monday ____________

____

____

____

____

____

____

3 Complete the sentences with a word from the box.

teach	has	gets up	~~go~~	finish	get

a I *go* to work at 8:00 a.m.
b She ________ at 7:00 a.m.
c You ________ work at 7:00 p.m.
d They ________ English.
e I ________ home at 8:00 p.m.
f He ________ lunch at midday.

4 Write three true sentences about your day.

I get up at 7:00 a.m.

____

____

5 Match the expressions with their meanings.

~~Good morning.~~	Good afternoon.
Good evening.	Good night.

a Hello.
Good morning
____
____

b Goodbye.
____

Writing

Building a description of a daily routine from notes

1 **Look at the notes about Stella's day. Complete the story of her day. Use the words in the box.**

get up, have breakfast	– 7:00
go to work	– 7:45
have lunch	– 2:00
finish work	– 7:30
get home	– 8:30
have dinner	– 9:30
go to bed	– 11:30

afternoon	bed	breakfast	dinner
evening	finishes	home	lunch
morning	~~up~~	work	

Her name is Stella Antonio.

She gets (1) ___up___ at seven o'clock in the (2) ____________. She has (3) ____________ and then she goes to (4) ____________ at 7:45. She has (5) ____________ at two in the (6) ____________.

She (7) ____________ work at 7:30 in the (8) ____________. She gets (9) ____________ at 8:30 and has (10) ____________ at 9:30. She goes to (11) ____________ at 11:30 at night.

2 **Choose a picture or a person from a magazine, the internet etc., and stick it in box A.**

- Imagine the person's daily routine.
  What time does he/she get up?
  Does he/she have breakfast in the mornings?
  Does he/she work or study?
  What time does he/she have lunch? etc.
- Complete the notes.

a

Put your picture here

____________	– get up
____________	– have ____________
____________	– go to ____________
____________	– have lunch
____________	– finish ____________
____________	– get home
____________	– have dinner
____________	– go to bed

3 **Write about the daily routine of the person in the picture in Exercise 2. Use the notes you made and Exercise 1 to help you.**

5 Places

Grammar

1 Complete the description with *there's* and *there are.*

Hi, I'm Mike. I'm from Yakima, in the USA.

Yakima is a beautiful city. (1) There are a lot of old buildings. (2) ________ a big park. (3) ________ two rivers, the Yakima and the Naches, and (4) ________ some lakes. Yakima is an interesting city. (5) ________ a famous museum, the Yakima Valley Museum.

(6) ________ three theaters and a lot of movie theaters. And every year (7) ________ a famous festival.

I love Yakima. It's a fantastic place!

2 Complete the sentences with *some* or *a.*

a There's __a__ statue in the park.

b There are ________ hotels near my house.

c There's ________ subway station near here.

d There are ________ people in the street.

e There are ________ stores near the museum.

f There's ________ new bar near here.

3 Complete the questions with *Is there* or *Are there.*

a Is there a pharmacy near here?

b ________ any restaurants near your English school?

c ________ a museum in your city?

d ________ a hotel near here?

e ________ any parks in your city?

f ________ any bars near your house?

4 Write short answers to the questions in Exercise 3.

a Yes, there is.

b No, ________.

c Yes, ________.

d No, ________.

e Yes, ________.

f No, ________.

5 Complete the questions with *any*, *a*, or *an.*

a Is there __a__ station near here?

b Is there ____ river in your city?

c Are there ____ stores near your house?

d Is there ____ movie theater near your English school?

e Are there ____ expensive hotels in your city?

f Is there ____ airport in your city?

6 Write true short answers to the questions in Exercise 5.

a Yes, there is. / No, there isn't.

b ________

c ________

d ________

e ________

f ________

Vocabulary

1 Label the places in the pictures with the words in the box.

bridge	lake	museum
park	river	square
station	statue	~~theater~~

a

b

c

d

e

f

g

h

i

a *theater* ________　　f ________
b ________　　g ________
c ________　　h ________
d ________　　i ________
e ________

2 Match the verb phrases with *go* to the words in the box.

~~the airport~~	the Empire State Building	
the city	the movie theater	the park
a show	the street	the zoo

a go to
the airport ________
____
____
____
____
____
____

b go for a run in
____
____
____

c go down
____

d go to the top of
____

3 Complete the sentences with the words in the box.

~~ATM~~	pharmacy	restroom	subway

a

b

c

d

Pronunciation

1 ▶ 16 Listen to the sounds /eɪ/ and /aɪ/.

/**eɪ**/ n<u>a</u>me
/**aɪ**/ l<u>i</u>fe

2 ▶ 17 Listen to the words in the box. Is the <u>underlined</u> sound /**eɪ**/ or /**aɪ**/? Put the words in the correct column.

~~ATM~~	convers<u>a</u>tion	<u>ei</u>ght	f<u>a</u>mous	
~~Friday~~	ins<u>i</u>de	l<u>a</u>ke	n<u>i</u>ght	n<u>i</u>ne
pl<u>a</u>ce	pr<u>i</u>ce	th<u>ey</u>	t<u>i</u>me	wh<u>i</u>te

/eɪ/	/aɪ/
ATM	Friday

▶ 18 Listen, check, and repeat.

Listening

1 19 **Cover the listening script. Listen and number the places in the order you hear them.**

church ☐

park ☐

bridge ☐ river ☐

tower ☐

museum ☐

Kelly: Do you know Paris, John?
John: Yes, I have an apartment near the river.
Kelly: What famous places are there?
John: In Paris? Everywhere is famous! Do you have Google Maps on your phone?
Kelly: Yes, I do.
John: OK, where's your hotel?
Kelly: It's just here.
John: OK, well there's a park near the hotel – the Luxembourg Gardens. It's very big. Do you like parks?
Kelly: Oh, yes. I love them. Are there any museums near the park?
John: Yes. The Louvre is near. It's a famous museum. And it's cheap – it's only ten euros to get in.
Kelly: Oh, good. That's cheap.
John: Yes, you go down this street and over the bridge – it's a very old bridge.
Kelly: OK. Is this the river Seine?
John: Yes, it's a beautiful river. And there are over thirty bridges across the river in Paris.
Kelly: Oh? Are there any other famous buildings near the river?
John: Yes. There's the Notre Dame – it's a church. I think it's ugly, but most people like it. It's near your hotel.
Kelly: Is the Eiffel Tower near my hotel, too?
John: No, it isn't. But there's a subway station near the Eiffel Tower.
Kelly: Is there a subway near my hotel?
John: Yes, there is. So you can take the subway and then go to the top of the Eiffel Tower. It's good, but it's expensive. It's seventeen euros to go to the top ...
Kelly: Seventeen euros? That's not expensive ...

2 Listen again. How does John describe each place in Exercise 1? Use the words in the box.

~~big~~	beautiful	cheap	expensive
old	ugly		

a the park *big*
b the museum ________
c the bridge ________
d the river ________
e the church ________
f the tower ________

3 Listen to John and Kelly again and underline the correct answer.

a John has **a house / an apartment** in Paris.
b Kelly **likes / doesn't like** parks.
c There are over **30 / 40** bridges in Paris.
d Kelly's hotel **is / isn't** near the Eiffel Tower.
e There **is / isn't** a subway station near Kelly's hotel.

6 Clothes

Grammar

1 Complete the sentences with the present progressive form of the verbs in the box.

dance	drink	~~eat~~
play	run	wear

A

She *is eating* an apple.

B

It __________ a jacket.

C

I __________ tennis.

D

They __________.

E

We __________ in the park.

F

You __________ beer.

2 Write true short answers to the questions.

a Are you sitting in the bathtub?
No, I'm not.

b Are you listening to music?
____

c Are you doing your homework?
____

d Are you wearing a T-shirt?
____

e Are you wearing sneakers?
____

f Are you having a great time?
____

3 Complete the table with the adverbs of frequency in the box.

not usually	sometimes	never
~~always~~	usually	

100%	*always*
0%	

4 Write questions.

a How often / you / eat fries
How often do you eat fries?

b How often / you / wear jeans
____

c How often / you / go to the movies
____

d How often / you / wear yellow
____

e How often / you / go to the gym
____

f How often / you / drink wine
____

5 Write true answers to the questions in Exercise 4.

a *I eat fries every day. / I never eat fries.*

b ______________________________

c ______________________________

d ______________________________

e ______________________________

f ______________________________

Vocabulary

1 Complete the color words.

a b l _ _
b b r o _ n
c g r _ _ n
d g r _ y
e o r _ n g e
f p _ n k
g r _ d
h y _ l l o w

2 Answer the questions.

a What color are my gloves?
They're black.
b What color is your cell phone?
____
c What color are your shoes?
____
d What color is your home?
____
e What color are your pants?
____
f What color is your pen?
____

3 Label the pictures with the words in the box.

boots	~~dress~~	hat	jacket	jeans	pants
shirt	shoes	skirt	top	T-shirt	

a *dress*
b __________
c __________
d __________
e __________
f __________
g __________
h __________
i __________
j __________
k __________

4 Complete the table with the words in the box.

a book	~~breakfast~~	coffee
a computer game	a cup of tea	an email
the housework	the guitar	the laundry
lunch	the paper	a phone call
the piano	soccer	tennis

make	play
breakfast	
read	**do**

Pronunciation

1 20 Listen to the sounds /oʊ/ and /aʊ/.
/oʊ/ clothes
/aʊ/ brown

2 21 Listen to the words in the box. Is the underlined sound /oʊ/ or /aʊ/? Put the words in the correct column.

~~brown~~	~~clothes~~	couch
homework	house	noun
old	outside	piano
tower	phone	yellow

/oʊ/	/aʊ/
clothes	brown

22 Listen, check, and repeat.

Writing

Posting on Instagram

1 Look at the Instagram posts. Complete the sentences with the words in the box.

~~looking at~~	walking	having	eating

marionjames

126 posts 166 followers 213 following

Edit profile

Marion James
#travel #vacations
#goodfood #thingsllove

Post 1

We're looking at Sydney Harbor. We're ________ a great time! #sydney #SydneyOperaHouse #SydneyHarborBridge

35 likes
1 DAY AGO

Post 2

Sam's ________ all these prawns! #AllYouCanEat #prawns @samsmith

18 likes
1 DAY AGO

Post 3

We're ________ on the beach every day. #beachwalk #summer

15 likes
1 DAY AGO

2 #sydney is a hashtag. Look at the hashtags in Post 1. Check (✓) the three correct tips for writing hashtags.

a Start with a hash (#). ☐
b Don't use capital letters. ☐
c Use words that tell more about the photo. ☐
d Don't put spaces between words. ☐

3 Look at the posts. Answer the questions.

a Where is Marion James?
____

b What is Sam eating?
____

c What do Sam and Marion do every day?
____

4 @username is a tag. Find the tags in the posts. Answer the questions.

a Who is eating prawns?
____

b Write your own tag. Use @ and a username.
____

5 Write posts for these photos taken near the Pyramids. Use tags and hashtags.

____
____
____
____
____

____
____
____
____
____

Notes

Notes

Macmillan Education

Companies and representatives throughout the world
American Inside Out Evolution. Workbook Beginner

D.R. © Macmillan Publishers, S.A. de C.V., 2017
Text D.R. © Sue Kay, Vaughan Jones, Peter Maggs and Catherine Smith, 2017
Adapted by The Content Station team: Simon Campbell, George Wells and Catherine Gray
Macmillan is a registered trademark.
First edition published 2017

ISBN 978-607-473-622-9

Based on New American Inside Out Workbook Beginner
D.R. © Macmillan Publishers, S.A. de C.V. 2008
Published under license from Macmillan Publishers Ltd.

Editorial Manager: Patricia Muradas
Editorial Operations Coordinator: Veronica Teodorov Ferreira
Editor: Cintia Zaitune
Concept design: Martha Tadaieski
Design: Jean Aranha
Page make-up: The Content Station
Illustration: Gustavo Gialuca pp 8, 10, 12
Graphic Production: Kelly Gobbo
Photographic research: The Content Station
Cover concept and design: Jean Aranha
Cover photo: Giovanni Gagliardi | Dreamstime

The authors and publishers would like to thank the following for permission to reproduce the photographic material:
Dreamstime / Shannon Fagan p4(tl), Dreamstime / Nyul p4(m), Dreamstime / Ben Ryan p4(b), Dreamstime / Eteimaging p5(la), Dreamstime / Issumbossi p5(lb), Dreamstime / Sofiia Kravchenko p5(lc), Dreamstime / Grafner p5(ld), Dreamstime / Ene p5(le), Dreamstime / Maksim Pasko p5(lf), Dreamstime / Lucadp p5(lg), Dreamstime / Jossdim p5(lh), Dreamstime / Tyler Olson p6(b), Dreamstime / Ogonkova p7(a), Dreamstime / Ogonkova p7(b), Dreamstime / Iamsunshine p7(c), Dreamstime / Kheng Guan Toh p7(d), Dreamstime / Jrtmedia p7(e), Dreamstime / Sergey Mayboroda p7(f), Dreamstime / Martinmark p8(a), Dreamstime / Ilovemayorova p8(b), Dreamstime / Alberto Jorrin Rodriguez p8(d), Dreamstime / Carafoto p8(f), Dreamstime / Monkey Business Images p11(2), Dreamstime / Antoniodiaz p11(3), Dreamstime / Wavebreakmedia Ltd p11(4), Dreamstime / Iakov Filimonov p12(mt), Dreamstime / Photographerlondon p12(b), Dreamstime / Mirko Vitali p14(5), Dreamstime / Rpianoshow p14(6), Dreamstime / Ian Allenden p14(8), Dreamstime / Sergei Denisov p14(9), Dreamstime / Dtiberio p15, Dreamstime / Pablo Hidalgo p16 (man), Dreamstime / Chris Boswell p16 (river), Dreamstime / Brett Critchley p17(IA), Dreamstime / Sureshr p17(IB), Dreamstime / Yorrico p17(ID), Dreamstime / Artisticco Llc p17(IE), Dreamstime / Scanrail p17(IF), Dreamstime / Ihar Balaikin p17(IG), Dreamstime / Sureshr p17(IH), Dreamstime / Ilona Reny p17(II), ameswimsel p17(rA), Dreamstime / Mimagephotography p17(rB), Dreamstime / Gabe Palmer p17(rC), Dreamstime / Brainsil p17(rD), Dreamstime / Anna Kucherova p18 (church), Dreamstime / Richard Mcguirk p18 (park), Dreamstime / Denis Pepin p18 (river), Dreamstime / Luca Di Fiore p18 (museum), Dreamstime / Jevtic p19(B), Dreamstime / Boggy p19(C), Dreamstime / Mark Hunt p19(D), Dreamstime / Georgerudy p19(F), Dreamstime / Mehmet Dilsiz p21(lt), Dreamstime / Jan Kratochvila p21(lm), Dreamstime / Pojoslaw p21(lb), Dreamstime / Debra Reschoff Ahearn p21(5b), Dreamstime / Threeart p21(rt); Getty Images / PhotoAlto / Laurence Mouton p4(tr), Getty / gchutka p6(a), Getty / 4FR p8(c), Getty / Image Source p8(e), Getty / Linka A Odom p8(g), Getty / Justin Case p10(b), Getty / David Sacks p11(1), Getty / Ron Levine p11(5), Getty / Bambu Productions p12(t), Getty / Don Mason p12(mb), Getty / Stanton j Stephens p14(1), Getty / Westend61 p14(2), Getty / Westend61 p14(3), Getty / Monty Rakusen p14(4), Getty / Peathegee Inc p14(7), Getty / Malte Mueller p17(IC), Getty / PhotoAlto / Sandro Di Carlo Darsa p18 (tower), Getty / Glowimages p19(A), Getty / Robert Daly p19(E), Getty / Westend61 p20(l), Getty / South_agency p20(m), Getty / Westend61 p20(r), Getty / ugurhan p21(5t).

CANIEM No. 2275

Macmillan Publishers S.A. de C.V. Insurgentes Sur 1886
Col. Florida, CP 01030
Álvaro Obregón
Ciudad de México
Tel: +52 (55) 5482 2200
elt@grupomacmillan.com

www.grupomacmillan.com www.macmillan.com.mx www.macmillanenglish.com

Printed in Brazil

This book was printed in September, 2017 by: Eskenazi Indústrica Gráfica Ltda, Avenida Miguel Frias Vasconcelos, 1023 - Jaguaré - São Paulo - SP.